I See Something...
Green

Inspired by Carl, who imagined
a different world for himself

By Marsha Bergstrom Georgiopoulos
Illustrated by Gail Diedrichsen

About the author and illustrator

Between them, the author and illustrator of *I See Something... Green*
spent over 60 years in the classroom. Marsha Bergstrom Georgiopoulos
taught Spanish while Gail Diedrichsen taught art. Both were also reading
instructors. On the very day they met, they felt a connection between their
major disciplines which produced many projects intertwining art and
Spanish. They also discovered a mutual respect for nature and all its
creatures. Upon retiring, a strong interest for teaming to prepare special
literature for young minds grew, and the two hope that more books will follow.

I See Something….Green written by Marsha Bergstrom Georgiopoulos and illustrated by Gail Diedrichsen dares the reader to imagine our world without the color green. Through beautifully written poetic prose, the author takes the reader on a journey that awakens the splendor and majesty of color in our lives. The lively illustrations capture the reader and bring the words to life on the page. *I See Something…Green* appeals to the youngest of children with its bouncy rhyme and youthful illustrations; however, it serves the older reader as a catalyst for discussion and the development of imagination. Finally, the book is augmented with a vocabulary page useful for academic skill building and cultural literacy. Written and illustrated by two veteran teachers, *I See Something….Green* attracts the youngest child as well as the child at heart. The first in a projected series, *I See Something….Green* is a valuable and cherished book to add to your collection.

Audrey Vaci
Gifted/Talented Teacher
English/Language Arts Teacher

As an educator, the best writing to me is writing that creates images and illustrations in our minds, igniting other ideas that can flourish. Marsha's poetry does just this and more! Her focus on color and the value of color in our world is something to which all children can relate. Her keen sense of discovery is evident as she walks the reader through a journey with a color. She also considers the child who may want to know more by providing an appendix which introduces them to extended vocabulary and language. Along with Gail's imaginative and intuitive illustrations, *I See Something …Green* is sure to become a treasured family or classroom favorite.

Dr. Kelley M. Kalinich
Superintendent
Kenilworth School District, No. 38, IL

Thanks, Dad - you showed me the joy that rhyme can bring to life.

Thanks, Gail - your persistent nudge to write is a gift I will forever treasure.

We also thank Audrey and Jennifer for their editing advice.

Imagine this world with no color green.
The strangest of worlds that anyone's seen...

Imagine this world with no color green.
Rainbows, for sure, would be very lean.

Winter to fall, no seasons between,
In a world that exists with no color green.

Imagine this world with no color green.
No lawn full of grass for a picnic serene..

A cactus with flowers a sight unseen...
In a world that exists with no color green.

Imagine this world with no color green.
Our tables would boast a less-tinted cuisine.

Holiday decor, surely less keen...
In a world that exists with no color green.

Imagine this world with no color green.
A gardening journal, such a dull magazine...

No forests with trees, quite a gloomy, sad scene...
In a world that exists with no color green.

Imagine this world with no color green.
No green grapes or apples, so fresh and pristine...

Or following a baby sea turtle's routine...
In a world that exists with no color green.

Imagine this world with no color green.
We'd not see green parrots naturally preen,

Nor a swimming frog with its watery sheen...
In a world that exists with no color green.

Imagine this world with no color green.
In a bowl of sweet candies, the lime ones unseen...

No geckos, no crocodiles dressed for Halloween...
In a world that exists with no color green.

By now you've discovered just what I mean
If green disappeared from Earth's delightful, big screen.
Great news I'll now share, so shake your tambourine,
Then dance and jump high over every ravine....

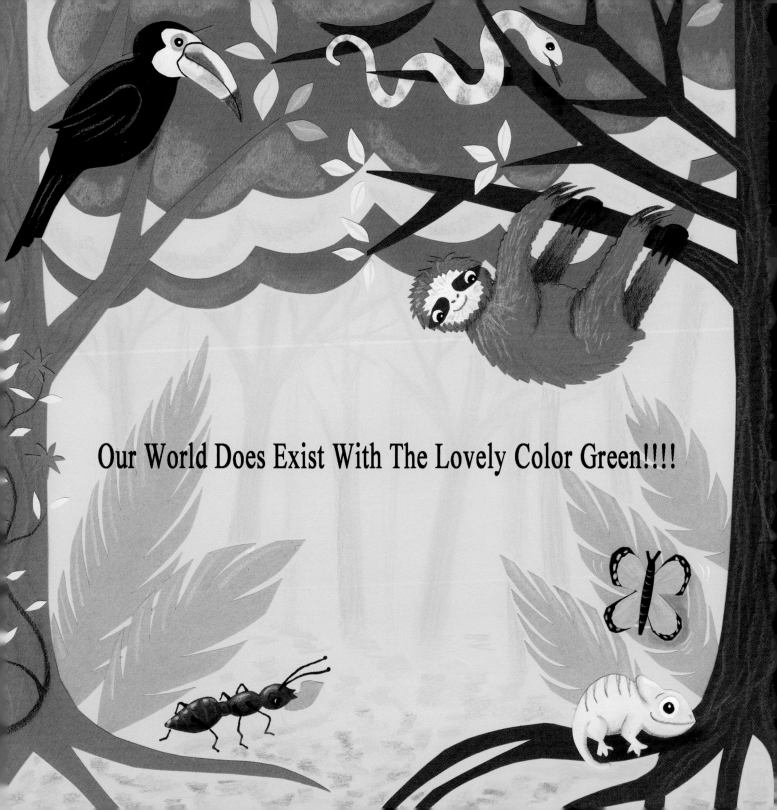

Our World Does Exist With The Lovely Color Green!!!!

Rainforests just might be the greenest places found on our planet. They are important. Trees and plants help to clean the air we breathe, while helping to regulate weather patterns. Each day new medicines are being made from rainforest plants; scientists are hopeful that many more will be discovered. Rainforests are home to more than half of all animals, insects, and birds on Earth. "Living Green" is something we can all do to help protect our environment. Recycling, buying foods and items that don't require cutting existing forests, planting new trees, and reading more about rainforests are all simple things each of us can do to keep our world a green place.

WORDS

Boast = possess or have an enjoyed item

Cuisine = style of cooking; prepared food

Emerald = a bright green stone used in jewelry - the stone of successful love.

Gecko = small tropical lizard

Journal = a magazine reporting on a special subject

Keen = bold and distinct

Lean = thin

Preen = to make yourself neat and tidy, especially birds

Pristine = clean and perfect

Ravine = small but deep valley

Serene = calm

Sheen = shine, shimmer

Shamrock = small plant with 3 leaves on each stem; national symbol of Ireland (It is the clover with 4 leaves that is associated with luck, though.)

Tinted = colored